WHO'S FARTED?

JINGLE SMELLS

First published in Great Britain 2022 by Farshore
An imprint of HarperCollins*Publishers*
1 London Bridge Street, London SE1 9GF
www.farshore.co.uk

HarperCollins*Publishers*
1st Floor, Watermarque Building, Ringsend Road
Dublin 4, Ireland

Written by Mara Alperin
Illustrated by Nicola Anderson

This book is an original creation by Farshore
© 2022 HarperCollins*Publishers* Limited

ISBN 978 0 0084 9520 6
Printed in Italy
001

A CIP catalogue record for this title is available from the British Library.

MIX
Paper from
responsible sources

FSC
www.fsc.org

FSC™ C007454

This book is produced from independently certified FSC™ paper
to ensure responsible forest management.

For more information visit: www.harpercollins.co.uk/green

CONTENTS

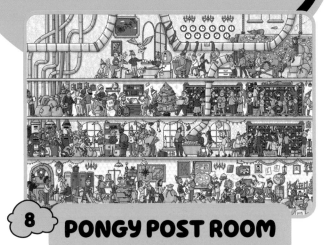

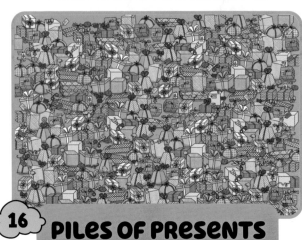

18 TRUMPY
TREE FARM

20 ROTTEN
REINDEER GAMES

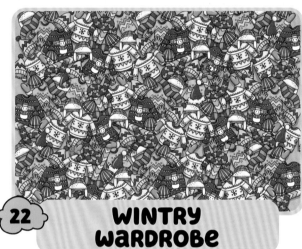

22 WINTRY
WARDROBE

24 JINGLE SMELLS

26 TOOTING
TINSEL TOWN

28 DECK THE HALLS

30 A VERY
FARTY PARTY

32 A NOT-SO-MERRY
CHRISTMAS

MEET THE FESTIVE FARTY FRIENDS!

Look out for these five chuffing characters in each busy scene ...

STINKY GRUFF THE GRUMPY ELF

He is the grumpiest, gassiest elf in the North Pole. He's usually found scowling and letting out smelly sputters.

BARTHOLOMEW BISCUIT

Bartholomew "Barty Farty-pants" is the gassiest gingerbread man you'll ever meet! He loves to sneak into Santa's kitchen late at night for a golden syrup bath. He may look sugary and sweet, but his pongy parps might put you off eating.

BLASTING BLITZEN

Blitzen is Santa's speediest reindeer. He loves to dash through the snow or race around the skies, propelled by his powerful festive farts! The other reindeer can't keep up (and they're happier staying further behind!).

PARPING PENELOPE

Unlike Gruff, Penelope is a happy-go-lucky penguin who loves slipping and sliding and dancing on ice ... but beware of her signature twirl-and-toot sequence! Penelope is a star with legendary super-stinks.

SQUEAK THE CHRISTMAS MOUSE

Santa's smallest helper is so excited for her first-ever Christmas! She likes shiny ribbons, sparkling decorations and loves letting out little squeaks ... from her bottom! Just like her farts, Squeak is small but mighty.

'TWAS THE NIGHT BEFORE CHRISTMAS ...

... and all through the North Pole, everyone is merry and bright as they get ready for Christmas Day.

Well, almost everyone.

Poor Stinky Gruff, the Grumpy Elf. He is gassy and grumpy, and down-in-the-dump-y. Nothing can make him smile. Nothing can make him laugh.

His friends have an idea – they'll borrow Santa's spare sleigh and fly around to visit all the Christmas festivities. Maybe they can spot something that will cheer up Gruff?

PONGY POST ROOM

Little Squeak brings the friends to Santa's post room. With all the jolly hustle and bustle, maybe Gruff will break a smile. But so far, he's just breaking wind! It's a good thing the window is wide open! Can you find all five Farty Friends, and these post room pieces?

3 ORANGE ENVELOPES

4 PAPER AEROPLANES

1 TYPEWRITER

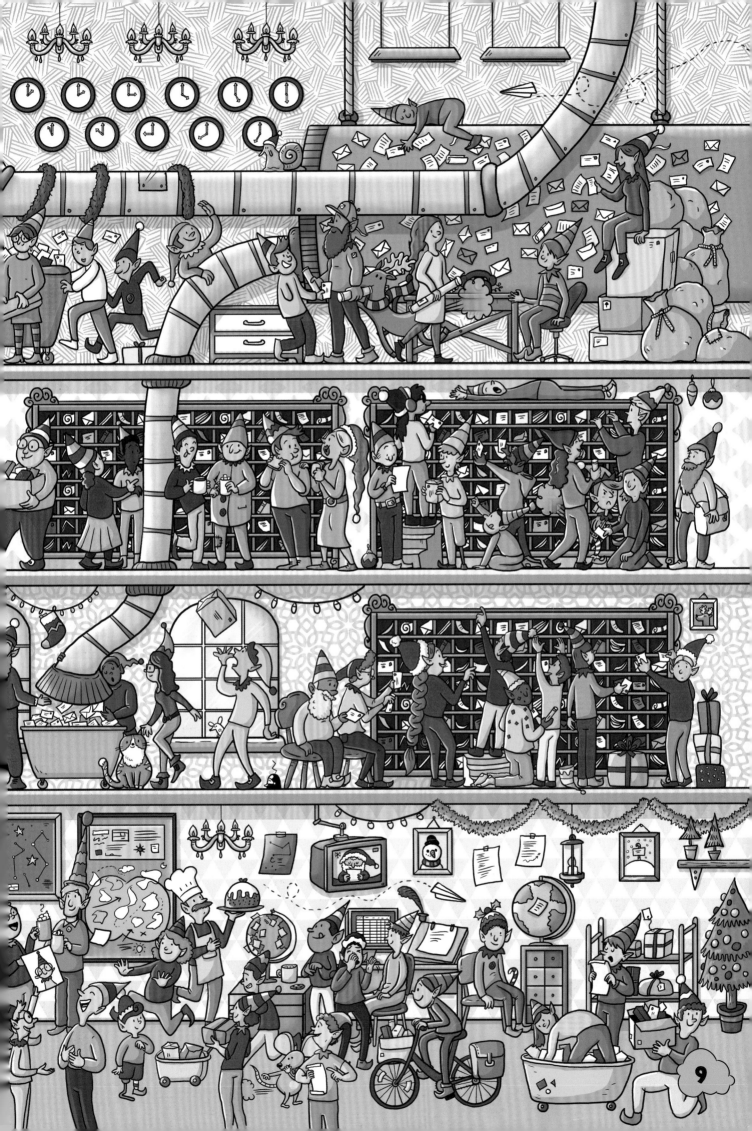

STINKY SKATING

Gruff is still grumbling, so Parping Penelope leads them to the skating rink for some slippery fun. But someone's left a stink in the rink, and another farter is blowing bottom bubbles in the hot tub … eww! Spot the five Farty Friends, and keep an eye out for these skaters:

3 FOXES

2 HARES PLAYING ICE HOCKEY

1 POLAR BEAR IN A PINK SCARF

TASTY TREATS

There's a delicious pile of Christmas treats, but will anyone still want to eat them after Bartholomew and the Farty Friends have parped the place up? See if you can spot them all, along with four not-so-stinky gingerbread men.

WHIFFY WORKSHOP

Can anything improve Gruff's grumpy mood? Perhaps a visit to Santa's workshop, where the elves are putting the finishing touches on the Christmas toys. But what's that stench? Has someone been niffy and naughty? Find all five Farty Friends, and these terrific toys:

3 NUTCRACKERS

3 TEDDY BEARS

1 ROCKING HORSE

PILES OF PRESENTS

There are four purple presents hidden somewhere in this mountain of ribbons and wrapping. Can you track them down, and then find the five Farty Friends as well? Try not to let their terrible trumps distract you ...

TRUMPY TREE FARM

While the Farty Friends are having a blast (and blasting out farts), Gruff is still down in the dumps. Will he cheer up at this tree-mendous tree farm? Or is he too busy cutting the cheese while the others are cutting down trees? Spot the Farty Friends and these festive farmyard animals:

3 SHEEP **3 DUCKS** **2 COWS**

ROTTEN REINDEER GAMES

It's time for Blasting Blitzen to compete in the Reindeer Games. There's skiing and sledding and snowball fights ... what more wintry fun could Gruff want? Let the games begin, but be careful who you stand upwind to! See if you can find all five Farty Friends, and these cool competitors:

2 SKIING REINDEER

1 SNOWBOARDING REINDEER

1 HULA-HOOPING REINDEER

WINTRY WARDROBE

Brrr ... it's getting chilly outside! Time to bundle up to keep warm and cosy. Can you spot the six Santa hats? And then find the five Farty Friends — quickly, before things get too whiffy!

23

JINGLE SMELLS

It's very busy backstage as the performers prepare for their spectacular Christmas Show. Maybe something here will make Gruff's spirits bright? Break a leg, everyone ... but watch out for anyone breaking wind! Can you spot all five Farty Friends, along with these peppy performers?

3 SINGING SNOWMEN

2 TUBA PLAYERS

1 FAIRY GODMOTHER

NORTH POLE

25

TOOTING TINSEL-TOWN

Gruff's friends haven't given up hope. They bring him to Tinsel-Town to turn his frown upside-down! But Gruff is still miserable ... and the townspeople aren't too happy either when things start to get super smelly! Keep a lookout for the Farty Friends, and these delightful decorations:

3 INFLATABLE SNOWMEN

3 GIANT SNOWFLAKES

2 GIANT LOLLIES

27

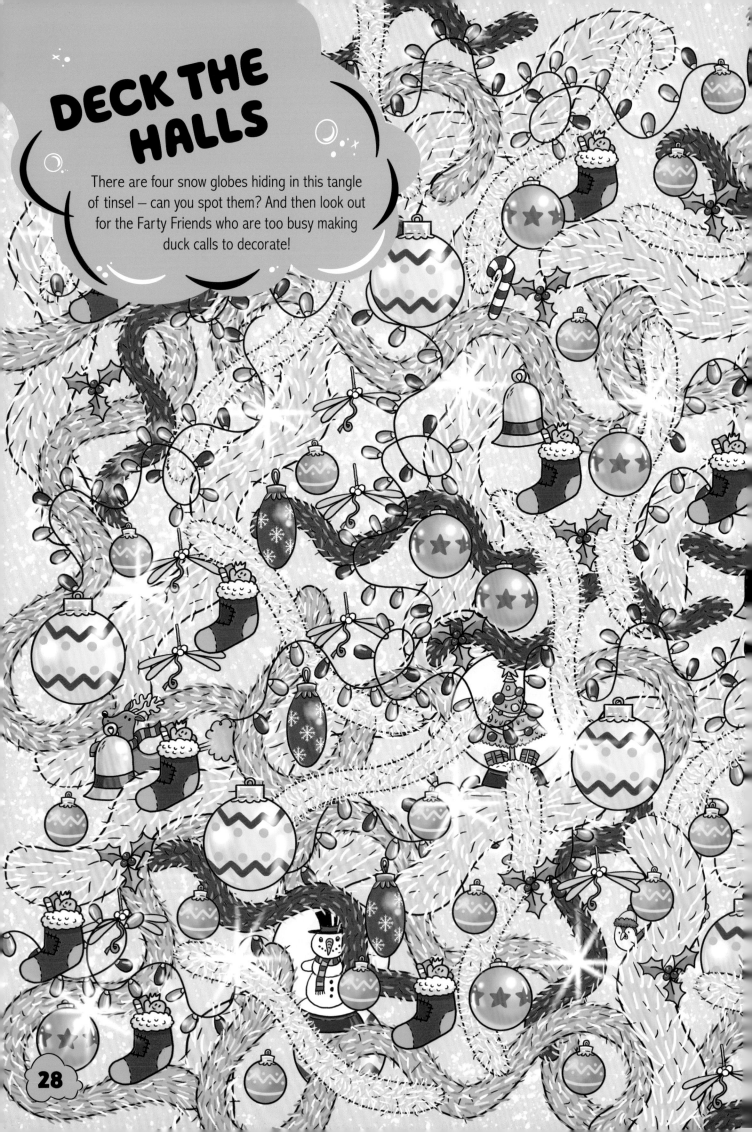

DECK THE HALLS

There are four snow globes hiding in this tangle of tinsel – can you spot them? And then look out for the Farty Friends who are too busy making duck calls to decorate!

A VERY FARTY PARTY

Back in the North Pole, it's time for the Christmas Eve feast. The food looks delicious ... but what's that smell? Hold your nose – the farters have just arrived! Stinky Gruff is still scowling, and his friends are worried that nothing will make him smile. Can you spot them all, and these festive feasters?

1 HAPPY HEDGEHOG

1 JOYFUL JAGUAR

MRS CLAUS

A NOT-SO MERRY CHRISTMAS

But poor Stinky Gruff the Grumpy Elf hasn't cheered up one bit. And then suddenly . . .

STINKY GRUFF IS SURPRISED

PFFFFFFFT!

Santa lets one rip.

Finally it looks like it will be a very Merry Christmas for everyone after all!

ANSWERS

8 PONGY POST ROOM

MORE TO FIND!

- [ ] A reindeer wearing spectacles
- [ ] Two workers enjoying sandwiches
- [ ] 2 cats
- [ ] A magnifying glass
- [ ] A remote-control car
- [ ] A Christmas pudding
- [ ] A cuckoo clock
- [ ] A postal sack with a leak

MORE TO FIND!

- [ ] A dropped ice cream
- [ ] 2 red Christmas crackers
- [ ] 2 ballerinas
- [ ] A man making an ice sculpture
- [ ] A bucket of fish
- [ ] A robin on skates
- [ ] A cosy sausage dog
- [ ] 2 human baubles

10 STINKY SKATING

TaSTY TReaTS

4 WHIFFY WORKSHOP

MORe TO FIND!

- [ ] 4 candy canes
- [ ] A U.F.O
- [ ] 5 mini Christmas trees
- [ ] A dinosaur toy
- [ ] An elf sleeping in a sleigh
- [ ] 4 snowglobes
- [ ] A unicorn on wheels
- [ ] A special visitor at the door

16 PILES OF PRESENTS

18 TRUMPY TREE FARM

MORE TO FIND!

- [ ] A mouse toasting a marshmallow
- [ ] A scarecrow
- [ ] A beaver gnawing a tree
- [ ] 5 pinecones
- [ ] A baby climbing a tree
- [ ] A person in a balaclava
- [ ] A squirrel
- [ ] A tree without leaves

MORE TO FIND!

- [ ] A bunny buried in the snow
- [ ] 4 green woolly hats
- [ ] Lost green mittens
- [ ] An out-of-place beach ball
- [ ] An egg-and-spoon race
- [ ] A woman with a stopwatch
- [ ] A Robin in a Santa hat
- [ ] 7 trophies

20 ROTTEN REINDEER GAMES

22 WINTRY WARDROBE

24 JINGLE SMELLS

MORE TO FIND!

- [ ] 4 pairs of red headphones
- [ ] Rapunzel
- [ ] A cow in two parts
- [ ] A face in a mirror
- [ ] A group of carol singers
- [ ] A rocking horse
- [ ] A large Xmas pudding
- [ ] A pear tree

26 TOOTING TINSEL TOWN

MORE TO FIND!

- [ ] Someone dressed as a Christmas tree
- [ ] A snowdog
- [ ] A giant muffin
- [ ] A dog in a stripey jumper
- [ ] A man who has decorated himself with tinsel
- [ ] A bird's nest
- [ ] 5 robins
- [ ] An inflatable Santa

DECK THE HALLS

A VERY FARTY PARTY

MORE TO FIND!

- [ ] A slice of blueberry pie
- [ ] A table of mice
- [ ] 4 salt and pepper shakers
- [ ] 2 hot chocolates
- [ ] 4 dropped pieces of cutlery
- [ ] 7 mince pies
- [ ] A Robin wearing a crown
- [ ] A dog blowing a party horn